C000022589

BOD'S NEW LEAF

by Alison and Lo Cole

MAKING A FRESH START

To the Bodfather

First published 2003 by Contender Books
Contender Books is a division of
The Contender Entertainment Group
48 Margaret Street
London W1W 8SE
www.contendergroup.com/books

This edition published 2003
1 3 5 7 9 10 8 6 4 2

ISBN 1 84357 076 9

Printed in Italy
Designed by Geoff Rayner
Production by Kate Gribble

The original Bod television programmes are also available on
DVD and Video from The Contender Entertainment Group

Here comes Bod.

And there he goes…

'I wonder why Bod's in such a mad dash,'
says PC Copper to Aunt Flo, Frank the Postman
and Farmer Barleymow.

When they catch up with Bod,
they ask him why he's in such a hurry.

'I've turned over a new leaf,' says Bod,
catching his breath. 'I've decided to go for a run
instead of a stroll. You should try it.'

'I'm not sure running is for me,' says Aunt Flo,
'but maybe I could do with a change.
I could take a trip to the art gallery…

or buy a new hat. That would turn a few heads.'

'Maybe I could do with a change,'
says PC Copper. 'I could turn in early
and catch forty winks…

That would make a change from
catching burglars.'

'Maybe I could do with a change,'
says Frank. 'I could turn up for work
on a racing bike…

That would be a special delivery.'

'And maybe I could do with a change,'
says Barleymow. 'I could turn one of my
fields over to wild flowers instead of barley…'

'Then you'd be Farmer not-so-Barleymow,'
they all laugh.

Later that day, Bod goes to Aunt Flo's for tea
to taste her new recipe – apple turnovers.

'These are delicious,' says Bod.
'They make a change from fruit cake.'
'Well a change is as good as a rest,' says Aunt Flo.
'And a rest is as good as a change,' smiles Bod,
who is glad to put his feet up after all that running.

After tea they wander into the garden
to admire Flo's fuschias.
Bod has some new thoughts on life –
his friends call them 'Bodisms'.

'The end of something…

is the beginning of something else.'

'Gather the fruits of life...

and life will be fruitful.'

'Smile more…

for more smiles.'

'Cleanliness is next to bodliness.'

'To be and not to be...

that is the answer.'

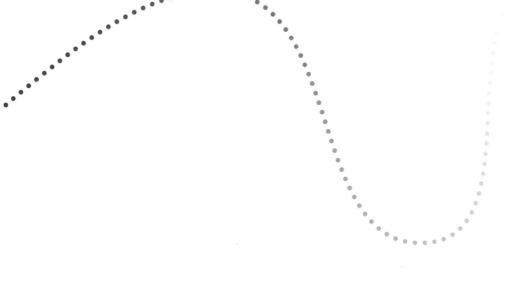

That night a strong breeze blows up.
'Even the weather's on the turn,' thinks Frank,
turning over in his bed.

Outside the leaves dance off the trees.

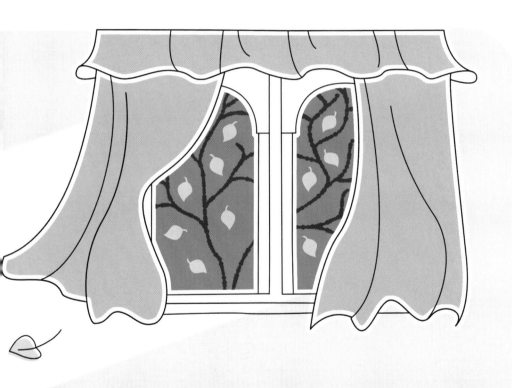

By the morning the wind is so strong
that it blows Aunt Flo's new hat away.

The weathercock on the church tower blows off and lands on PC Copper's helmet.

The knock makes him feel so dizzy that he spins round and round.
He has turned into a weathercop!

At Barleymow's farm all the leaves have blown off the trees and Barleymow has raked them into a huge pile.

When Bod comes down the lane, he slips on the leaves and falls head over heels.

'You said you wanted to turn over a new leaf,' jokes Barleymow. 'Now an old leaf has turned you over!'

After the wind comes the rain, and after the rain come the first flakes of snow.

The snow falls through the night and when everyone wakes up the village is covered in a thick white blanket.

'Who needs a new hat when we've got a new world?' says Flo to Bod.

Barleymow swaps his plough for a snow plough.

PC Copper and Frank have the day off –
and make a snowman.

'It's Aunt Snow,' they tell Bod.

Aunt Flo makes them all come inside
for a mug of steaming hot cocoa.

'Some things never change,' thinks Bod.

As the snow melts, Bod watches for the first
shoots of Spring. 'Look,' he says one day,
'the trees are in bud.'

'In bod, you mean,' smiles Aunt Flo.

On his farm Barleymow is planting new seeds.

Frank and PC Copper go for a
bicycle race through the blossoms.

You can't see their pedals for petals.

Soon the weather is so warm that
Aunt Flo suggests a trip to Bodley Bay.

'I think we could all do with a change of scene,'
she says.

When they get there, the tide is low
and the sun is high.

Bod and Flo watch flocks of gulls and geese through Bod's Bodnoculars.

PC Copper, Frank and Barleymow paddle in
rock pools, looking for whelks and winkles.

'Makes a change from looking for clues,' says PC Copper.

When the tide turns, it's their turn to go.

'Come along, Bod,' calls Aunt Flo.
'What on earth are you doing?'

'I'm turning over a new Bod,' he says.

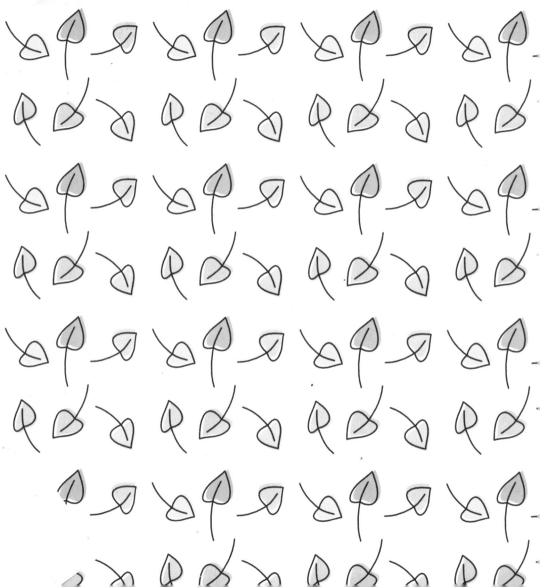